Tansy Smith

by
Helen
Orme

illustrated by
Anthony
Williams

FULL FLIGH

Titles in the FULL FLIGHT runway » series

Level 3

Goal!	Jane A C West
Too Hot	Roger Hurn/Alison Hawes

Level 4

A Big Catch	Alison Hawes
Deyda's Drum	Roger Hurn
The Strawberry Thief	Alison Hawes
Billy's Boy	Melanie Joyce

Level 5

Cage Boy	Jillian Powell
Master Blaster	Melanie Joyce
Game Player King	Stan Cullimore
In the Zone	Tony Norman

Level 6

Dodgems	Jane A C West
Tansy Smith	Helen Orme

Level 7

Pirate Attack	Jonny Zucker
Hitting the Basket	Jonny Zucker

Badger Publishing Limited
Suite G08, Business & Technology Centre
Bessemer Drive, Stevenage, Hertfordshire, SG1 2DX
Telephone: 01438 791037 Fax: 01438 791036
www.badger-publishing.co.uk

Tansy Smith ISBN 978 1 84691 856 8

Publisher: David Jamieson
Editor: Danny Pearson
Design: Fiona Grant
Illustration: Anthony Williams
Printed and bound in China through Colorcraft Ltd., Hong Kong

I Hate School!

Contents

Badger Publishing

Vocabulary

Traveller   Different
Hated   Campaign
Robbers/Robbed   Council

Main Characters

Tansy

Sam

Dave

Chapter 1
You've Got To Go!

"I hate school!"

"You know you've got to go to school, Tansy.
We will all be in trouble if you don't."

Tansy's family had just moved to the Traveller site.

At every town they travelled to Tansy had to go to school. She hated it!

This time, she was going to a secondary school for the first time. She didn't like that idea!

The teachers were very friendly.

"Tansy is new to the school. Look after her, please," said the form tutor.

But the other children didn't like Tansy. A boy called Dave was rude to her.

"I know where you come from," he said. "You come from that Traveller site. We don't want your sort here."

One of the girls was friendly. Her name was Sam.

"Don't listen to the others," Sam said. "They are horrid to me too. I'll help you if you like."

Sam helped Tansy a lot. She showed her where everything was in the school.

Tansy wasn't good at making friends. But she really liked Sam.

Tansy thought the lessons were boring.
She sat at the back and didn't listen.

She spent her time drawing doodles in her
book. This made the teachers cross, but Tansy
didn't care.

"Her work is very poor," the teachers said to
each other. "It's probably because she
changes schools every
time she moves."

Chapter 2
The Robbery

One day when Tansy got to school there was a police car outside.

The head teacher told them there had been a robbery at the school.

Some of the school's computers had been taken.

"I bet it was your lot," Dave said. "And I bet you told them where the computers were." Some of the class believed what Dave had said. But Sam didn't.

Tansy had met up with Sam in town. She was walking back to the Traveller site.

She walked past the library. An old van was parked nearby.

The library was closed but she could see people inside. What was going on?

Just then an alarm started to ring.
Two men rushed past Tansy.

They were carrying computers.

One of them bumped into her.

"Out of my way!" he shouted.

The two men jumped into the van and drove off.

Chapter 3
What Do You Know About This?

Tansy heard a police car coming.
At first she wanted to run. But she stayed
where she was.

"If I run, they will think I did it," she thought.

Two police officers jumped out of the police car.

"What do you know about this?" one of them
said to Tansy.

A police woman spoke to Tansy.

"I want you to tell me what you saw," she said.
"Did you get a close look at the men?"
"Tell me what they looked like."

But Tansy found it hard to find the right
words. Then she had an idea.

"I'll draw them for you if you like," she said.

The next day was a special day at school for Tansy.

Her drawings were so good the police had caught the robbers.

They were the same men that had robbed the school.

Most of Tansy's class thought Tansy was brilliant, but Dave didn't say anything.

Mrs Turner was the art teacher at the school. She asked Tansy to show her some of her drawings.

"You have a real talent," she said. "I'll give you extra lessons if you like."

Tansy was thrilled. This was just what she wanted to do!

Tansy rushed home to tell her Mum and Dad about it.

But the news wasn't good.

"I'm sorry, Tansy. Don't you remember? We're moving on next week," Dad said.

Would Tansy ever see the school again?

Save Our Site!

Contents

Chapter 1
Back to School

"Tansy's back!"

Everyone crowded round. When Tansy had
first come to the school last year no-one had
liked her, except her friend Sam.
This time it was very different.

"How long are you back for, Tansy?" Sam asked.

"My Dad's fruit picking on lots of farms, so we may be here for the whole summer."

"That's great!" said Sam

Mrs Turner, the art teacher, was pleased to see Tansy again.

She knew that Tansy was really good at art.

"Would you still like to do those extra lessons?" She asked.

"Yes please!"

Tansy started her art lessons straight away. Sam came too, but she couldn't draw as well as Tansy!

Mrs Turner gave Tansy all sorts of things to draw.

She liked to draw people.

"You are really brilliant at people's faces!" Mrs Turner said.

"I wish I was as good as you."

Chapter 2
Bad News

One day when Sam came to school she found Tansy crying.

"What's the matter Tansy?" Sam said.

"Everyone at the Traveller site got a letter yesterday," Tansy said.

"We can't stay there anymore. We've got to move on. Dad will have to find work somewhere else. And I'll have to go to a different school."

Sam was really upset to hear the news.

She tried to make Tansy feel better.
"Maybe you can have art lessons at your new school," she said.

"I don't want to go to a new school! I want to stay here and have lessons from Mrs Turner!" Sobbed Tansy.

The next day Sam had news for Tansy.
"My Mum read about the Traveller site in the paper. Someone complained to the council about it. And I know who it was.
It was Dave's Dad!"

Dave was in Sam and Tansy's tutor group.
He was always horrible to Tansy.

All the others in Tansy's class were really angry. They didn't want Tansy to go.

"Let's have a campaign to save the site!" someone said. "We'll make posters, have a protest, anything we can think of!"

"Great!" Sam said. "And I know just the person to draw the posters!"

Chapter 3
A Famous Artist

Soon posters saying 'Save our Site' went up all over town.
Mrs Turner had helped with copying them.

Tansy had drawn pictures of people who lived at the site to go on the posters.

People in the town thought the drawings were really good.

"They must have paid a famous artist to draw these," they said.

Some of the posters were printed in the paper.
A reporter came to the school to talk to Tansy.

People in the town were amazed to find out
that a young girl had drawn the pictures.

Then came the big day when Tansy was
interviewed on television!

It was very scary but Tansy did really well.

"All we want is somewhere to live," Tansy said.

"The site isn't doing any harm, so why can't we stay there?"

A man from the council was interviewed too.

"The site has got to close," he said.

"We need the land for new houses.
But we've decided to open a new site on the other side of town. We'll make sure it has everything you need, and we won't close the old site until it is ready."

Months later, Tansy was on TV again.

She was standing by the gate of the new site.

Tansy was asked to cut a tape to show the site was open.

People were busy taking photographs.

Tansy looked proudly at the sign.

Questions

Who was rude to Tansy at her new school?

What was the name of the art teacher?

Who appeared on Tansy's posters?

What was the name of the new Traveller site?

What would you campaign for?